Contents

Babe:
Pig in the City

Adapted from the novelization by
JUSTINE KORMAN and RON FONTES
Based on the motion picture screenplay written by
GEORGE MILLER JUDY MORRIS MARK LAMPRELL
based on characters by
DICK KING-SMITH

Level 2

Retold by John Escott
Series Editors: Andy Hopkins and Jocelyn Potter

Pearson Education Limited
Edinburgh Gate, Harlow,
Essex CM20 2JE, England
and Associated Companies throughout the world.

ISBN 0 582 36400 0

First published in the USA by Random House, Inc. 1998
First published by Puffin Books 1998
Third impression 2001

Typeset by Digital Type, London
Set in 11/14pt Bembo
Printed in Spain by Mateu Cromo, S. A. Pinto (Madrid)

Published by Pearson Education Limited in association with
Penguin Books Ltd, both companies being subsidiaries of Pearson Plc

For a complete list of the titles available in the Penguin Readers series please write to your local
Pearson Education office or to: Marketing Department, Penguin Longman Publishing,
5 Bentinck Street, London W1M 5RN.

Introduction

Mrs Hoggett said goodbye to her husband.

'I'll be careful – I won't lose the pig,' she said, before she and Babe drove away.

But plans can go wrong. When she and the little pig leave the farm for the city, they have to stay at the Flealands Hotel – a hotel with animals in most of the rooms!

Here Babe meets Fugly Floom, the clown. And some very strange animals – a monkey, some chimpanzees, and an orang-utan!

'This is the city,' Bob, the chimpanzee, tells him. 'Nobody wins in the city. And nobody helps anybody. Understand?'

But Babe will always help other animals when he can. And sometimes this can be dangerous!

Funny and exciting things happen when the famous little pig goes to the city.

This is the story of the film, *Babe: Pig in the City*.

The Sheep-Pig, by Dick King-Smith, was the first book about Babe. That, too, was a film – *Babe: A Little Pig Goes a Long Way*.

Some of the Animals in the Story

Sheep

Pig

Duck

Monkey

Chimpanzee

Orang-Utan

Bull Terrier

Dobermann

Poodle

Mice

Chapter 1   A Clever Little Pig

Babe is a pig – a very clever little pig. He can bring sheep home as quickly as a farm dog can. He and his friend, Farmer Hoggett, were famous before this story began.

But famous little pigs are not always careful . . .

When Farmer Hoggett was at work one day at the bottom of the well on his farm in Hoggett Hollow, Babe watched him from the top. Suddenly, the wall broke and the not-very-careful Babe fell into the well! And a large stone fell with him! Down . . . down they went, and then – CRASH! – the pig and the stone fell on to Farmer Hoggett's head!

After the accident, Farmer Hoggett stayed in bed. His head

The farm at Hoggett Hollow.

1

Farmer Hoggett in the well.

hurt, but he was not angry with Babe. The next day Mrs Hoggett had to do her husband's work on the farm, and she was not happy.

She was outside when she saw a black car. It stopped and two men got out. She ran to the farmhouse.

'Oh!' she cried. 'Oh, dear! Oh, Arthur! It's the men from the bank! They want their money.'

She ran inside and looked quickly through some papers on her husband's desk. He watched her from his bed. She found a letter and began to read it to Farmer Hoggett.

'"Your pig . . . to visit us and work with some sheep . . . we will send plane tickets . . . we will pay . . ."' And there was a large number of dollars after the word 'pay'.

Mrs Hoggett was excited. 'Listen!' she said to her husband. 'I'll take the pig and they'll pay me those dollars. We can give the money to the men from the bank. Then the bank won't take the farm!'

She called, 'Pig, pig!' and the farm dogs, Fly and Rex, heard her. They went to find Babe.

The little pig was with Ferdinand, the duck.

'Babe, you have to go with the boss's wife,' said Fly.

'You can't go,' Ferdinand told Babe. 'I want you here. You're the nicest pig on the farm and my best friend.'

'Babe, the men from the bank are going to sell the farm,' said Fly. 'We'll all have to go away.'

'And not every farmer is as kind as ours,' said Rex.

'But what can I do?' asked Babe.

'You're a sheep-pig,' said Rex. 'They'll want you to work with sheep for money. Do your best.'

In front of the farmhouse, Mrs Hoggett shouted, 'PIG!' then turned to her husband. 'Arthur, you call the thing!'

Farmer Hoggett spoke quietly and kindly, 'Come, pig.'

Babe looked at Fly. 'I don't want to leave you,' he said.

'The boss's wife will be with you,' said Fly.

So Babe walked across to the farmhouse, and into Mrs Hoggett's arms. Ferdinand and the dogs followed.

'I want that pig here!' said the duck, angrily.

'Can you come with me?' Babe asked Fly. 'Please ...' He began to cry.

'They want you, not me,' said Fly. He moved near the little pig. 'Now stop crying, and don't be afraid.'

Mrs Hoggett said goodbye to her husband.

'I'll be careful – I won't lose the pig,' she said, before she and Babe drove away.

And so the little pig left his home on the farm.

He didn't see Ferdinand in the sky above him.

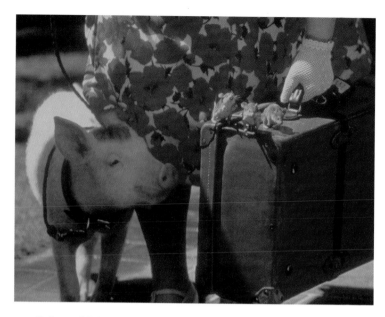

Babe and Mrs Hoggett start their journey to the city. Three little mice go with them.

Chapter 2   At the Airport

The big plane started to move away from the airport. At the back, with the bags, Babe sat in his little box. He tried not to be afraid. Mrs Hoggett sat at the front of the plane, but she did not see Ferdinand outside the window. Then the plane moved up into the sky. Ferdinand flew after it as fast as he could. But it got smaller and smaller and soon he could not see it.

Then Ferdinand heard some birds behind him.

'Did you see that big fast thing?' he asked one of them. 'Where's it going? Do you know?'

'Yes,' said the bird. 'Follow us.'

◆

At the end of the journey, somebody took Babe's box off the plane and put it into a small room with a lot of bags and boxes. A dog came in and pushed his nose everywhere. The words 'drug finder' were on the dog's jacket.

'Excuse me,' said Babe. 'Is my Human outside? She's –'

'Look, friend, I'm busy,' said the dog. Then he looked carefully at Babe. 'You're a strange dog.'

'I'm not a dog, I'm a sheep-pig,' said Babe. 'I want my Human, and I'm hungry, and –'

'Yes, yes, that's very sad,' said the dog. 'But I'm working. I have to smell all these bags and boxes. And when I smell drugs, I have to make a lot of noise. Then the humans run in here.'

'They do?' said Babe. 'Why?'

'I don't know,' said the dog. 'But then they give me some nice food! Watch!'

The dog stood near a bag and made a loud noise. Some men

Babe meets the 'drug finder' dog.

from the airport ran into the room.

'Which bag? Which bag?' they said. 'This bag?'

They took a bag away.

Some minutes later, Mrs Hoggett saw some airport detectives with her bag.

'Esme Cordelia Hoggett?' a detective asked.

'Yes!' said Mrs Hoggett. 'Thank you for the bag. Now, I have to find my pig and catch my next plane, and –'

'We've got the pig,' said the detective.

'Well, let's go then,' said Mrs Hoggett.

The men took her into a little room, and there was Babe. He was in the middle of a table under a camera. This camera took pictures of everything inside the bags and boxes from all the planes, *and* inside animals.

A woman spoke to Mrs Hoggett.

'Esme Cordelia Hoggett,' she said, 'I'm an airport detective. We think you're carrying drugs.'

And before Mrs Hoggett could say anything, she had to take off her clothes.

♦

Hours later, the farmer's wife left the little room with her pig. She did not have any drugs, of course, but now it was too late for her next plane. And there was no plane home again for two days.

Mrs Hoggett started to phone hotels in the city, but each hotel said, 'No animals.' After this, she and Babe tried to sleep at the airport, but one of the workers there said, 'No animals in the airport! This isn't a farm!'

Mrs Hoggett and Babe went out into the busy street.

'Wait!' somebody called. It was a night cleaner at the airport. He gave Mrs Hoggett a paper, then went away again quickly. On the paper there was the name of a hotel: 'The Flealands Hotel, 349, Random Canal.'

Chapter 3   The Flealands Hotel

The Flealands Hotel was tall and very old, and it was in a little street next to the river. A woman opened the door.

'I and ... er ... my pig want a room,' said Mrs Hoggett.

'We don't take animals!' shouted the Landlady. 'Go away!'

Mrs Hoggett stood outside for a minute, then walked down another little street at the back of the hotel. Suddenly she heard somebody. The Landlady was in the street, behind her.

'How long do you want to stay?' she asked quietly.

'Two days,' said Mrs Hoggett. 'But you said –'

'Oh, that was for the people round here,' said the Landlady. 'I don't want them to know about my animals.'

She took Mrs Hoggett and Babe into the hotel, and they climbed up some stairs. On the first floor, Babe looked through a

The Flealands Hotel.

half-open door – and saw two brown eyes! On the next floor, he
turned and saw two dogs. Their names were Nigel and Alan. A
third dog, Flealick, came out between them. His back legs were
on wheels.

Flealick ran across and smelt Babe. 'Dog . . . er . . . no. A cat!' he
said. 'No cats on this floor!'

When they got to the top floor, Babe saw a lot of cats. The
Landlady said to Mrs Hoggett, 'Never open the front door. The

Some of the animals in the hotel.

phone is downstairs. And remember, the little pig has to stay in the room at all times.'

She took them into a room and, after a minute or two, Mrs Hoggett went downstairs. She wanted to make a phone call to her husband.

'Stay, pig,' she told Babe, and pulled the door shut behind her.

Babe jumped on to a chair and looked out of the window at the city.

'When will I see my first sheep?' he thought. 'Or perhaps I'll have to do something different here.'

The door opened quietly behind him. A small monkey ran in and looked round the room with large, brown eyes. His name was Tug.

'Hello,' said Babe.

Tug did not answer. He jumped on to the bed and pushed

Babe looks out of the window . . .

9

. . . and Tug takes Mrs Hoggett's bag!

Mrs Hoggett's bag on to the floor. Three little mice from the farm jumped out before Tug pulled the bag out through the door.

'Wait!' shouted Babe, and he ran after the monkey.

Tug pushed the bag down to the next floor and jumped after it. Babe ran after him, but Tug ran down to the next floor with the bag. He went quickly into one of the rooms and shut the door after him.

'Open this door!' shouted Babe.

The door opened again, and Babe saw a chimpanzee with a fat stomach, in a pretty dress. Her name was Zootie. 'Do you want something?' she asked.

Babe did not understand. 'This is an animal,' he thought. 'So why is she wearing human clothes?'

'Who is it, dear?' asked somebody inside the room.

Babe looked past Zootie and saw her husband, Bob. He also had human clothes on, and he did not take his eyes away from the TV.

Zootie looked at Babe. 'It's . . . er . . . a strange thing.'

'He can come in,' said Bob, in a friendly way.

Babe went in. 'I want the bag,' he said.

Bob looked at Tug, then at Babe. 'Do you want to make him sad?' he said, and Tug started to cry.

'But . . . it isn't his bag,' said Babe.

'Who says it's yours?' asked Bob.

A smaller chimpanzee in trousers said to Babe, 'I don't think you're listening to my big brother.' His name was Easy, and he was Bob's younger brother.

Babe looked at all three chimpanzees. 'I know I'm small,' he said. 'But I can be dangerous when I'm angry.'

Babe meets the chimpanzees: Bob, Zootie and Easy.

Somebody behind Babe said loudly, 'What's this?'

Babe turned and saw a large orang-utan in a black coat and trousers! The orang-utan's name was Thelonius.

'We're talking to this strange animal,' said Bob.

'He's from a different country,' said Zootie.

'Perhaps from a different world,' said Easy.

'You stupid animals!' said Thelonius. 'This is a pig!'

'Excuse me, but I'm a sheep-pig,' said Babe. 'And I want my bag – now!'

Thelonius and the chimpanzees suddenly moved back. Babe turned and saw a human in the room. The man wore dirty old clown's clothes, and his name was Fugly Floom. He looked at the little pig.

'Uncle Fugly!' shouted the Landlady from outside the room. 'Uncle Fugly!'

The clown quickly put the pig into a box, then went out of the room. The Landlady and Mrs Hoggett were on the stairs.

Fugly Floom smiled, and the Landlady said, 'Fugly, this is Esme Hoggett. Esme Hoggett, this is my uncle, Fugly Floom.'

'I can't find my pig!' cried Mrs Hoggett. 'Who took my pig? We have to call the police!'

'No!' cried the Landlady. 'No police! That will be the end of this place.'

Inside Fugly's room, Babe put his head out of the box and cried, 'That's my Human!'

'Be quiet!' said Thelonius, and pushed him into the box again.

Outside, Mrs Hoggett said, 'I can go home without my clothes, but I can't go home without the pig!'

Fugly Floom made some strange noises. 'He's saying, "A pig ran out of the hotel",' the Landlady told Mrs Hoggett. 'Where did it go? To the beach, he thinks.'

Mrs Hoggett turned and ran down the stairs. Then she ran out into the streets.

Chapter 4   Problems for Fugly

Mrs Hoggett walked through the streets of the city. 'Pig ...
Pig ... PIG!' she called.

Two policemen were in a police car when she walked past
them. 'Pig, pig, pig, pig!' she called.

People looked at her. 'She's calling those policemen pigs!' they
said. The policemen started their car and began to follow Mrs
Hoggett.

She turned left and went down a little street. 'Pig, pig ...'
she called. Five young men and women looked at her. One
young man came across the street. He had Rollerblades on his
feet.

'Who are you calling a pig?' he said.

'I'm looking for my husband's pig,' said Mrs Hoggett.

'Oh, yes!' said the young man.

Then he saw her bag and tried to take it. He pulled – and Mrs
Hoggett pulled. Then she ran, and she pulled the young man after
her on his Rollerblades!

The four other men ran after them.

When she got to the end of the road, Mrs Hoggett pulled the
young man on Rollerblades in front of the moving police car!
The car turned quickly and went CRASH! into a man. The man
stopped washing his shop window. He fell, and his water went all
over Mrs Hoggett!

Next, a girl on Rollerblades went past the farmer's wife – fast!
– and pulled Mrs Hoggett's bag out of her hand.

Mrs Hoggett sat unhappily in the road. Water ran down her
face and clothes. When she looked up, the two policemen were
in front of her.

'Oh, dear!' she said.

♦

That afternoon, Fugly Floom took his chimpanzees and Babe to a hospital in the city.

'I have to make the children in the hospital happy for an hour,' said the clown.

Babe waited inside a box-on-wheels with a paper pig. Easy sat on top of the clown's box and said to Babe, 'Remember everything! You'll be OK. Then Fugly will pay you.'

Suddenly the box moved, and Fugly Floom pushed it out in front of the children.

Easy began cutting the 'pig' in half. Babe's head looked out of a hole in the front of the box, and the paper pig's legs came out of a hole in the bottom. To the children, of course, these were Babe's legs.

When the box was in two halves, pigs' meat fell out of it! The children laughed loudly.

A minute later, Easy put a plate on the table. The plate had a big cup over it. Easy took off the cup – and there was Babe's head, on the plate!

The children laughed again.

Fugly put the cup on the plate and walked away with them. Babe's head came up through the hole in the table. 'Am I doing it right?' he asked.

Zootie pushed his head down again. 'Not now!' she said.

And the children laughed.

Next, Fugly put a heavy black ball into a big gun on wheels. Babe walked out from under the table.

'Go away before the children see you!' said Thelonius.

Fugly lit the gun, and turned it to the children. Then he shut his eyes and put his fingers in his ears. Easy quickly turned the gun to Fugly, and the children started to laugh. They waited for the gun to go BANG!

Suddenly Fugly turned. He fell over the pig – CRASH! – and the light in his hand started a small fire. There was a loud BANG!

from the gun, and water came from the ceiling! The water quickly put out the fire, but people and animals started to run everywhere!

In the middle of all this, Thelonius helped Fugly up from the floor. 'Oh, dear!' said Thelonius.

♦

Later, at the hotel, Fugly ate everything in the kitchen of his hotel room – chicken, cakes, chocolates. Then Thelonius took the clown into the next room and sat him in a chair. Minutes later, Fugly was asleep.

The chimpanzees jumped on to the kitchen table and started to eat chocolates. But Thelonius came and took the box away from them.

'When do they pay me?' Babe asked him. 'I did everything. I got in the box, I put my head through the hole. Where's my money? My Human will be here soon, and I have to get the money for the farm.'

Thelonius did not answer. He went into the next room and watched TV.

'You want your money?' said Bob, quietly.

'Yes,' said Babe. 'Where is it?'

Bob looked up to a small open door in the ceiling. Easy started to laugh, but Zootie stopped him quickly.

Then the chimpanzees made some 'stairs' up to the door in the ceiling. They used boxes, an old TV and a chair.

'I can't climb up there,' Zootie told Babe. 'I'm going to have some babies soon.'

Babe was afraid, but he started to climb.

They all heard the phone. In the next room, Thelonius put the phone to Fugly's ear, and the clown heard, 'Why did you use a pig? You stupid clown! I'll never find any work for you again. This is the end, Floom, do you hear me? This is the end!'

In the kitchen, Babe was on a chair. It was very high, and very dangerous.

'I – I think I'll come down now,' he said.

'No, no!' said Bob. 'You're nearly there!'

Very slowly, Babe moved up. After a minute, he was at the top! 'W–what do I d–do now?' he asked.

Bob smiled at Easy. Easy laughed and ran out of the kitchen. Then Bob pushed the 'stairs'! They moved one way . . . then the other way . . . and then they came down with a big CRASH! Babe came down with them, but he went out through an open window – and into the river!

He swam through the cold water to the hotel, and Zootie opened the front door for him.

'That wasn't funny!' said Babe.

When he was in Fugly's room again, Babe went to see Thelonius. The orang-utan wanted to take the chocolates away from the chimpanzees, and he was angry.

'I'm wet!' cried Babe. 'Look at me!'

'Give me the box of chocolates,' Thelonius told Bob.

'Why do you always help the Human?' asked Zootie.

'He gives us clothes,' said Thelonius, 'and he teaches us to do things. Other chimpanzees can't do them.'

'BUT HE DIDN'T PAY ME!' shouted Babe.

Thelonius got really angry then. He threw Babe out of the window again, into the river!

The tired little pig went up to Fugly's kitchen again.

'There isn't any money for me,' he said to Bob. 'There was never any money. Is that right?'

'Right,' said Bob. 'This is the city. Nobody wins in the city. And nobody helps anybody. Understand?'

Babe went sadly to his room at the top of the hotel and looked out of the window into the night. He looked at all the lights across the city.

'Where is the Boss's wife?' he thought.

◆

The next morning, Babe woke up and heard voices downstairs. He went out and looked down the stairs. Fugly Floom was in the arms of men from the city hospital. His face was white and his eyes were closed. The Landlady was with them.

The hotel was very quiet. When the animals saw strangers, they always hid. But when the front door closed after the men from the hospital and the Landlady, they all came out from their rooms.

'I couldn't wake Fugly up,' said Thelonius, sadly.

'He'll be all right,' said Easy. 'He's always all right.'

♦

Ferdinand the duck was in the city after a long journey with the other birds. He flew round it for more than an hour, but then he was tired. He stopped on the top of an old church.

'Pig,' he called. 'P-pig . . .'

Chapter 5   Dangerous Dogs

Babe was hungry. He went out of his room and looked down. Bob was there with the dogs.

'Any food?' Bob asked them.

'No,' said Flealick.

'Sorry, no,' said Nigel and Alan.

'Cats! Have you got any food?' shouted Bob.

Four cats opened a door near Babe and started to sing, 'No, no, no, no. We haven't any food.'

Zootie looked at Bob, and her husband said, 'We're going to get some food. I know a place.'

Zootie was afraid. 'Are we going outside without a human?' she said. 'It'll be dangerous.'

'We'll be careful,' said Bob.

The chimpanzees left, but Babe could not stay in the hotel. He had to eat! Now!

The chimpanzees moved quickly between the street lights, next to the river. Then Bob stopped suddenly and looked back. He saw Babe under a street light.

'Get out of that light!' he called.

'Where's the food?' asked Babe. 'I have to eat.'

'Be quiet!' said Bob.

'I'll work for food,' said Babe.

'What can you do?' said Easy.

'I can move sheep from one place to another place,' said Babe.

'Go home, dear,' said Zootie.

'Wait a minute,' said Bob. 'Perhaps I can find him some sheep. Then he can move them, and we can get the food. Let's go.'

The animals came to a shop two streets away from the hotel. Babe followed the chimpanzees round to the back, to a small hole in the wall.

'They're in there,' Bob told Babe.

'Border Leicester sheep?' asked Babe. 'Scottish Blackface sheep?'

'Bull Terrier and Dobermann,' answered Bob.

Babe did not know sheep with those names, but he started to go through the little hole. 'Where do you want me to put them?' he asked.

'That isn't important,' answered Bob. 'But we don't want them to see us when we get the food.'

'OK,' said Babe. He went through the hole in the wall.

'Hello?' he called. 'Hello? Is anybody here?'

The Dobermann – a large black dog – came out from behind the wall.

'Go away,' he said to Babe. 'Or are you stupid?'

'I – I'm looking for some sheep,' said Babe, suddenly afraid.

Then a noise from something worse came from behind the

Two dangerous dogs!

Dobermann. The noise of an angry, dangerous dog – a bull terrier. It ran at Babe.

Babe turned and ran. The bull terrier came after him and the Dobermann followed. They all went through the hole in the wall, but Babe's little legs were not as fast the bull terrier's and the Dobermann's. The dogs got nearer and nearer!

Babe got to the door of the Flealands Hotel. 'It's me!' he shouted. 'Open the door!'

The bull terrier jumped! Babe moved quickly.

Tug opened the door of the hotel and saw the dog with Babe. The little monkey quickly shut the door again.

Babe got away from the bull terrier, but he nearly ran into the Dobermann. He turned quickly and ran down a dirty little street. Cats and dogs were asleep in boxes. They were animals without homes. Babe ran past them, then he saw some old TVs and radios at the back of a shop. He ran in between them and hid.

The bull terrier and the Dobermann stopped.

'Where is he?' said the Dobermann.

'Listen!' said the bull terrier.

The dogs waited quietly. Then they looked up and saw Babe above their heads, on top of a box.

'There!' said the bull terrier. 'After him!'

And the little pig ran again. He ran into a garden, through the flowers and small trees. 'I can't see anything!' he cried.

It was dark in the garden, but the bull terrier could see two eyes. He jumped at them!

'Aaagh! Stop! It's me!' cried the Dobermann. 'I'm your friend!'

But the bull terrier was too angry. He could not stop now.

The Dobermann ran!

Babe went into the next garden. Three chimpanzees watched him from a tree. They had food from the shop in their arms. Easy gave his food to Zootie, then climbed down the tree to Babe.

The bull terrier ran into the garden, and Easy jumped up into the tree again. Babe tried to climb the tree, too, but he could not do it. So he ran.

At the hotel, Thelonius looked out of a window and saw the bull terrier and Babe. The dog's open mouth was very near Babe's back now. And Babe's feet moved slowly.

The chimpanzees watched from the tree. Nigel and Alan and the other animals at the Flealands Hotel watched from windows. The cats and dogs without homes, near the water now, watched too.

The bull terrier threw Babe into the river and jumped in after him. But the dog forgot one thing – he could not swim. His head went under the water.

Thelonius, Babe and the other animals watched. The bull terrier tried to push his head above the water, but he could not.

Suddenly, Babe started to swim across to a small boat. The other animals watched. The little pig pushed the boat under the dog, and the bull terrier climbed into it.

Babe swam to dry ground and got out of the river. The animals without homes ran across to him – they wanted to meet this famous little pig. Famous now because he helped the bull terrier.

One dog – a poodle – came to talk to Babe.

'Can you help *me*?' she said.

'How can I help you?' said Babe.

'I haven't got a home,' said the poodle.

'And I'm hungry!' cried a little cat.

'I-I d-don't h-have a H-human!' cried a small dog.

All these animals without homes wanted Babe to help them.

'Please, sir, help us,' cried the poodle. 'We don't have anywhere to go.'

'Well . . . it's nice and warm inside the hotel,' said Babe.

Bob, the chimpanzee, moved nearer. 'That's not a good idea,' he said.

'But they –' began Babe.

'No!' shouted Bob. 'No, no!'

An old dog saw the food in Bob's hand. 'Is that food?' he asked. He got very excited and began to dance round the chimpanzee.

'Food! Food! Food!' cried the other animals.

'Be quiet!' shouted Thelonius from a window above them. 'Somebody will hear you.'

'Perhaps we could all go inside,' said Babe. 'There's some food for everybody.'

'Stop!' said Bob. 'Who's boss here?'

'*He* is,' said somebody.

Everybody looked round and saw the bull terrier.

'The pig is boss now,' said the dangerous dog. 'OK?'

'OK!' said everybody. They looked up at Thelonius.

The old orang-utan smiled. 'He's only a pig,' he said. 'And he'll always be a pig.'

The animals without homes all went inside the Flealands Hotel. The other animals watched them carefully. Nigel and Alan were not happy.

'They're not *clean*, Alan,' said Nigel.

'You're right, Nigel,' said Alan.

The last animals without homes came into the hotel. Then Babe heard, 'Pig, I want to thank you.'

He turned and saw the bull terrier.

'That's very kind of you, but –' began Babe.

'I'm not kind,' said the bull terrier. 'Bull terriers aren't kind. I have to be dangerous.'

'But you can change,' said Babe.

'I can't,' said the dog. 'Bull terriers are born to be dangerous. To kill.'

Babe tried to understand, but it was difficult.

Chapter 6   Animals Everywhere!

That night, Zootie's babies were born. Easy soon saw something wonderful in her arms – the two little heads and four little ears of two baby chimpanzees.

'I'm an uncle!' he said.

'And I'm a father!' cried Bob.

And they laughed.

'They've got their father's ears,' said one of the dogs.

Thelonius looked but he said nothing.

The bull terrier said, 'Be quiet, everybody. Perhaps the Boss wants to say something. So *listen*.'

He looked at Babe.

Babe and his new friend, the bull terrier.

'Er – what can I say?' Babe began. Then he started to sing. 'La, la, la. La, la, la . . .'

The bull terrier sang with him, then the hungry cat, and the poodle. Soon everybody began to sing, as loudly as they could.

'LA, LAAAAA!'

'Shhh!' said Thelonius. 'Somebody will hear you.'

But nobody heard him.

'LA, LA, LA, LAAAAA!'

♦

The sound went across the river, over the tops of houses, to the top of a church. Here, Ferdinand listened – and got very excited!

'I know that song!' he said.

And the duck flew away and followed the sound of the music.

23

But Ferdinand was not the only person to hear the animal noises.

'Listen, Roger!' said a woman in a house across the river. 'There are a lot of dirty animals in that place! We have to do something! We have to tell the police.'

Babe stopped singing when he saw the duck's face at the window. He ran and opened it.

Ferdinand flew in and said hello. Then he looked round at the others and said, 'Who are these animals?' He saw the bull terrier. 'Who's this?'

'I'm his friend,' said the bull terrier, dangerously.

'Oh,' said Ferdinand. 'That's nice.' He looked at Babe. 'What's happening here?'

Suddenly, the front door opened with a CRASH! and people ran into the hotel. Some were policemen, and one was a woman doctor in a white coat.

'Look upstairs,' she told a policeman.

A man talked quietly and kindly to a cat, and his friend gave some food to the poodle.

'Don't go with them,' said the bull terrier, but the poodle did not listen. She wanted more food and she followed the man out of the door.

'There's nobody up here!' the policeman called from upstairs.

'It's time to go!' cried Ferdinand.

But the duck flew into the hands of a policeman.

'Look!' laughed the policeman. 'Here's *my* dinner!'

Babe ran to help his friend, but the policeman laughed again. 'And here's my breakfast!'

But now the bull terrier jumped on the policeman and started to fight.

Cats and dogs ran out of the hotel and into the streets. Some got away, but other animals ran into the hands of policemen.

Three policemen got on top of the bull terrier, and one put

Suddenly ... people ran into the hotel.

something over the dog's head. Babe watched, but he could do nothing with a policeman's hand on his back.

Ferdinand hid under a chair.

The men soon caught Bob, Zootie, Easy and the two new baby chimpanzees. And soon after that they caught Flealick on his wheels.

'Do something, Thelonius!' cried Zootie.

The orang-utan turned away. He walked past Babe and went up to Fugly's room.

'You did this!' he said to the pig, angrily.

A minute later a policeman pushed open the door of Fugly's room.

'Come and look at this!' he called to the other policemen.

Thelonius was in his black coat and trousers, and he had a small bag in one hand.

The policemen moved nearer to Thelonius. Babe watched. 'Be careful,' said one of them. 'Orang-utans are very strong.'

One man went behind the orang-utan, then they all ran at Thelonius at the same time. The big animal did not try to fight and, very soon, they took him away.

A policeman pulled Babe behind him, to the front door of the hotel. Suddenly, Ferdinand flew down to the ground floor – on to the policeman's head! The policeman gave a small cry. He looked up, and walked into a table. The table, the flowers on it, and the policeman all fell to the floor with a CRASH!

Babe ran upstairs to Fugly's room, but the policeman came after him. Babe looked for somewhere to hide, because he could not get past the big man. Then he had an idea! Quickly, he ran to the open kitchen window – and jumped out!

Down . . . down . . . and into the river went Babe.

♦

Outside the hotel, the policemen put all the animals into a big van. Nigel and Alan watched. One of the men pushed Flealick into the back.

'We have to do something,' said Nigel. 'Who will look after Flealick? It's dangerous when he goes too fast on his wheels. Who will give him the right food?'

'You're right. We'll have to go with him,' said Alan.

So the two dogs ran to the back of the van and jumped in. But somebody said, 'We can't use this dog. Look at him.' Then strong hands threw Flealick *out* of the back of the van, and a man shut the doors.

But now Nigel and Alan were *inside*!

Flealick ran to the van. The doctor got in. The little dog jumped up and caught the bottom of her dress in his mouth. She tried to pull it away from him, but she couldn't. So she shut the door on her dress and the van moved away. The van pulled Flealick behind it, with the dress in his mouth!

Babe was out of the river now. He saw Tug, the little monkey, near a tree, and the two of them watched Flealick.

'What's he doing?' said Babe.

'He'll have an accident!' said Tug. 'Let's go!'

They ran after the van.

On top of the Flealands Hotel, Ferdinand the duck watched them.

'Pig, pig. What are you doing?' he cried, and he flew after them.

Babe and Tug could not catch the van. But when it turned right into the next road, it threw Flealick off – with the bottom of the dress in his mouth.

Babe and Tug ran across the road to him.

'Flealick, are you all right?' said Babe.

Flealick could not answer with the dress in his mouth.

Tug pulled it away.

'It's OK,' Flealick said. 'I can remember their smell. We can follow it and find them.'

Babe and Tug stood Flealick on his wheels again, and the little dog put his nose to the ground. 'They went this way,' he said. He looked at the road to the hotel.

Babe put *his* nose to the ground. 'No, Flealick,' he said. 'I think they went that way.'

Ferdinand flew down from the sky. 'What are you doing?' he said to Babe. 'Pig, listen to me. They aren't nice people. You're only a little pig in the city. What can you do? What can *anybody* do?'

Babe thought for a minute. Perhaps the duck was right. Perhaps he *couldn't* help. He was only a pig.

He looked at Flealick. The little dog moved away as fast as he could on his wheels. He wanted to help his friends.

Babe turned to Tug. 'Are you coming with me?' he asked.

'Yes, I'm coming,' said Tug. The little pig went after Flealick, and Tug followed.

'You're stupid!' said Ferdinand.

But he went after them.

Usually, Babe only used his nose when he wanted to find food. But now he followed the smell of the animals in the van. There were a lot of other interesting smells in the city – fish, coffee, new bread, and the smells of different people. But the little pig did not look at the shops or offices, the cars or the rivers or the people of the city. He was too busy.

Then he said, 'I think we're here.'

And there was the van, outside the University Hospital.

Babe's nose took the four friends to a window. Tug climbed up the wall and looked inside the room. He saw a man with a camera.

Babe uses his nose and follows his friends.

28

Thelonius stood near one wall, but he did not have any clothes on. The man took photographs of Thelonius, then he turned his camera to the new-born chimpanzees.

Tug looked into the next window and saw a lot of mice in boxes. Quickly, he climbed down to Babe, Flealick and Ferdinand. They were under the trees near the hospital.

Tug talked fast. But before he finished, Flealick said, 'Let's go and get them!' He started to move, but Babe stopped him.

Two humans in white coats went past the animals. When they were inside the hospital, Babe said, 'We have to be careful!'

Chapter 7   Mrs Hoggett Flies!

After the two policemen took Mrs Hoggett to the police station, they asked her a lot of questions. She was there all night. But the farmer's wife was more unhappy about her little pig than about the policemen's questions.

In the end, an important police detective came to see her and she told him her story.

'I thought, "What will Arthur say when he hears about the pig? And what's happening to the dear little animal? Esme Hoggett, you can't do anything right!"' she told him. She looked at the detective. 'That pig is my husband's best friend. So when I get out of here, I'll start looking again!'

The detective looked hard at Mrs Hoggett. 'That woman can use a lot of words in a very short time!' he thought. 'But I think she's a good woman really.'

He also liked pigs, because his father had a farm.

To Mrs Hoggett he said, 'All right. You can go.'

♦

Babe and his friends found a way into the hospital research building, and to the rooms upstairs. Here, researchers used different animals for their work.

Tug found a dark room.

'I think this is it,' said Tug, and he opened the door.

Babe looked into the dark room. 'Hello?' he called.

'It's the pig!' cried Bob.

'It's the thing!' said Zootie.

'Boss!' said the bull terrier.

'Shh!' said Babe. 'We have to be quiet.'

But the animals were excited. Tug quickly helped the chimpanzees out of their boxes, and then they all helped the cats and dogs out of *their* boxes.

Flealick hid under the stairs and watched. Two researchers carried a box to a big van. Then one of them started to go up the stairs!

'I'll go and lock the door,' the man said.

Flealick wanted to shout to the other animals, but he was afraid to open his mouth.

Upstairs, Ferdinand said, 'OK, OK, the fast animals come with me, the other animals wait here. If they die, we can get away.'

'Ferdinand!' cried Babe.

'Well, then we don't *all* die,' the duck said.

Babe turned to the others. 'We'll *all* go, quietly and carefully,' he said.

'But very fast!' said Ferdinand. 'Let's go!'

'Where's Thelonius?' asked Easy.

The orang-utan pulled on his shirt.

'What are you doing?' Bob asked him.

'I'm dressing,' said Thelonius.

Babe said quietly, 'Mr Thelonius, we have to go now.'

'Not ... without ... my clothes,' he said.

'Thelonius, you're an orang-utan,' said Zootie.

Thelonius thought, '*Am* I an orang-utan, or am I a human? I don't know.'

Suddenly, the animals in the room heard a noise on the stairs.

'Be quiet!' said Nigel.

'Shh!' said Alan.

They all tried to hide in the dark room. Easy pulled Thelonius with him, and they waited, afraid.

The researcher opened the door and looked round. His eyes were too tired and he did not see anything. He shut the door again. Then he locked it and went away.

Thelonius slowly put on his coat.

♦

Across the city, Mrs Hoggett went into the Flealands Hotel. The door was open, and the flowers and the table were on the floor inside.

'What happened here?' she thought. She called, 'Pig? Pig, pig, pig, pig!' but there was no answer.

Then she heard a noise upstairs and ran up to Fugly's room. The Landlady was in a chair by the window.

'Is the pig here?' asked Mrs Hoggett.

'No,' said the Landlady. 'There are no animals here.'

'What happened, dear?' asked Mrs Hoggett.

'This was a nice street when I first came here,' she said, unhappily. 'People helped me, and I helped them. We were friends. What's happening to the world? I'm away one night, my Uncle Fugly nearly dies, and –' She began to cry.

The farmer's wife put an arm round her.

'I wanted to make a nice place for the animals,' the Landlady told her. 'But I was stupid. What did the animals do to *her*?'

'Who?' asked Mrs Hoggett.

'Her!' said the landlady, angrily. 'That woman in the house across the river! She called the police!'

'Right!' said Mrs Hoggett. 'Can I wear some of your clothes? My dress is dirty.'

Some minutes later, Mrs Hoggett ran out of the hotel in Fugly Floom's clown clothes! She pulled the Landlady behind her.

They ran over the bridge to the house across the river.

'WE WANT OUR ANIMALS!' shouted Mrs Hoggett, when the woman opened the door.

♦

The animals climbed up chairs and boxes to a door in the ceiling of the hospital room. It was the only way out of the room.

When they were between the ceiling of the research room and the floor of the room above it, the animals moved carefully. The pig walked in front.

'Where are we going?' asked one of the dogs.

'Where *can* we go?' said the poodle. 'Where in the world *isn't* dangerous?'

'Yes, is there anywhere for my babies?' said Zootie.

'There is a place, but it's a long way from here,' said Babe. 'Everybody is kind and good there.' The little pig thought about the farm and his friends there. 'But is it there now? I don't know.'

The animals moved above the ceilings of other rooms and came out on to a little bridge. The bridge went across to the Children's Hospital.

'Let's go,' said Babe, and the others followed him across the bridge.

One little boy was not asleep. His eyes opened wide when a pig, chimpanzees, dogs, cats and a duck walked quietly past the other children. And for the first time in his life, he saw an orang-utan. The boy smiled!

But he could not see out of the window, so he did not see Mrs Hoggett and the Landlady.

They arrived at the hospital gardens on Fugly Floom's

bicycle-for-two. When Flealick ran out of a door, they followed him.

Inside the Children's Hospital, the little boy went after the animals. He climbed to the top of some stairs – but they were on their way down to the ground floor.

A doctor came to the little boy and said, 'Hello, little boy. What are you doing here?'

The little boy looked down the stairs and said, 'Duck.'

The doctor laughed. 'Duck? No, no!' he said. 'Come with me, I'll take you to your bed.'

Of course, the boy was right. There *was* a duck on the stairs. He and the other animals got to the bottom of the stairs – and they were in the hospital kitchen!

In the kitchen, the cook had a red face and was not a very happy man. He had some plates and cups in his hands when he suddenly saw the animals. 'Aaagh!' he cried – and all the plates and cups fell on the floor with a loud CRASH!

Mrs Hoggett, the Landlady and Flealick heard the noise, and the sound of shouting men – and a *pig*! The two women and the dog went quickly to the kitchen. Waiters and the cook ran after the animals, and the animals ran out of a door.

Mrs Hoggett ran faster than everybody. Her fingers were nearly on her wonderful little pig – and then the cook caught the braces at the back of her clown-trousers. He pulled her into the kitchen with a SNAP! noise.

But Babe was happy. The Boss's wife was here!

'It's *her*!' he shouted happily. 'Ferdinand, the Boss's wife is here!'

But the duck didn't hear him. 'Look, pig!' he said.

Babe turned and his mouth fell open. They were in a very big room, with balconies. In the middle of the ceiling a big light – a chandelier. There were long tables across the room, and at the tables were some of the city's most important people. The women wore long dresses, and the men wore black coats and trousers and white shirts.

Cooks in white trousers and shirts stood next to a table of food. A waiter sat on a very high chair, next to a mountain of wine glasses.

The room went very quiet. The people looked at the animals – and their eyes and mouths opened very wide. Then, very slowly, the cooks and waiters began to move across the floor to the animals. They wanted them in the kitchen.

But Ferdinand did not want to go in the kitchen, and he flew across the tables. The other animals ran everywhere! Babe hid under one of the ladies' long dresses, and all the important people began to shout and run.

Bob and Zootie took their babies and started to climb up to a balcony. Suddenly, some doors on to the balcony opened, and

The women wore long dresses . . .

Her braces caught on the chandelier, and she flew across the room!

out came Mrs Hoggett and the Landlady. The Landlady ran down the stairs from the balcony, but the farmer's wife called, 'Pig! Come, pig!'

Babe and Ferdinand came out from under two long dresses and looked up. Mrs Hoggett shouted, 'I am Esme Cordelia Hoggett, and I'm here for Arthur's pig!' – and she jumped!

Her braces caught on the chandelier, and she flew across the room!

The braces got longer – and Mrs Hoggett went down ... down ... Then she came up again with a SNAP! noise. But without her pig.

The cook from the kitchen got Babe and started to run to the kitchen doors. Mrs Hoggett flew across the room again on the chandelier – and hit a table of food. The food table hit the cook's back and pushed him into a table of people. Babe flew out of his hands and fell into a plate of cakes!

'Come, pig! Come, pig!' Mrs Hoggett shouted, and she flew across the room again by her braces.

The cook jumped up, and caught one of her legs. He turned her round and round, very fast!

'We have to stop him, Ferdinand!' cried Babe.

The pig ran across the floor and into the cook's legs. The cook fell back – and pulled off Mrs Hoggett's shoe!

The farmer's wife flew across to the mountain of glasses. The waiter fell off the high chair into a plate of food.

Three policemen and two waiters tried to catch Babe. Mrs Hoggett flew to the balcony again, ready to jump on them. Opposite her, on a second balcony, the cook also got ready to jump.

'I'll stop her,' he said.

The farmer's wife jumped. The cook jumped . . . and they met with a CRASH! in the middle of the room. Thelonius ran to Mrs Hoggett and helped her to the balcony again.

Then the farmer's wife heard a cry. It was Babe! One of the policemen had the little pig in his arms. The policeman looked up and saw Esme Hoggett. She was on her way down from the balcony. The farmer's wife took the pig from his arms and flew to the balcony with it again.

The animals below shouted happily. Mrs Hoggett laughed and flew from the chandelier again, Babe in her arms. She was so happy – she had her pig again! But – oh dear! – Thelonius jumped with them, and the three of them were too heavy for the chandelier. It began to break away from the ceiling!

It went down to the floor with a CRASH! Mrs Hoggett, Babe and Thelonius went with it.

Round the room, important people started to come out from under the tables.

'This is a strange party!' they laughed.

But Zootie was not so happy. She could not find one of her babies. 'I can't find my baby!' she cried.

Babe looked up at the ceiling. High above him, in the hole from the chandelier, something moved. And there was the little chimpanzee!

'There he is! Oh, he's going to fall!' cried Babe. 'Thelonius! Catch him!'

The little chimpanzee started to fall. Thelonius moved quickly under him – and caught him!

'Oh, thank you, Thelonius!' said Zootie. She ran across and took her baby.

'Yes, thank you,' said Bob.

Thelonius looked at Bob, then said, 'Thank the pig. Thank the pig for everything.'

Chapter 8   A Happy End

It was many weeks later.

Loud music came from the old Flealands Hotel now. The word DANCELANDS shone in lights outside the building.

Across the river, a woman and her husband put their fingers in their ears, but they could not shut out the loud music.

'The animals were better than this noise!' the man shouted to his wife.

'Yes, they were,' she shouted, unhappily. 'Oh, why did I call the police that night?'

♦

But changes are better for some people than for other people.

The farmer's wife and the Landlady were happy. The Landlady didn't have a hotel now, but with the money from the building she and all the animals moved to Hoggett Hollow. The men from

Three mice, at home again.

the bank had their money too, so they were happy!

Nigel, Alan and Flealick went to live with the Landlady in a little house near the farm.

Bob, Zootie, Easy and the baby chimpanzees found a home outside in the trees.

But Thelonius went to live in the farmhouse, and he watched Mrs Hoggett all the time. The farmer's wife now had a friend for life.

Babe and Farmer Hoggett were, of course, *very* happy. They were in the same place again. And there were no more problems with the well. The water was clean and ran fast.

The two of them stood at the top of the well and looked down. Then the farmer turned to his pig and said, 'Everything's all right now, pig. Everything's all right.'

ACTIVITIES

Chapters 1–2

Before you read

1 Why is Babe a famous little pig? Do you know?
2 Why is a city *not* a good place for a pig?
3 Find these words in your dictionary. They are all in the story. What are they in your language?

   drug   farm   human   smell   soon   stone   well

After you read

4 Who or what are these?

   a Babe   **d** Ferdinand
   b Mrs Hoggett   **e** the 'drug finder'
   c Fly and Rex   **f** Flealands

5 Work with another student.

   Student A: You are Babe. You are visiting Farmer Hoggett in bed after his accident. How do you feel? Tell him.
   Student B: You are Farmer Hoggett. You can't remember much about the accident. Ask Babe about it. How do you feel? Tell him.

Chapters 3–5

Before you read

6 What will Mrs Hoggett and Babe find in the Flealands Hotel?
7 Find the words in *italics* in your dictionary.

   a Which words are
      – people?
      – things?
      ceiling   clown   hole   landlady   Rollerblades   wheel
   b Why do people or animals *hide*?

After you read

8 Use the best question-word for these questions, then answer them.
   What   Where   Why   Who

39

a ..... tells Mrs Hoggett to go away?

b ..... does Tug take from Babe's room?

c ..... doesn't the Landlady want Mrs Hoggett to call the police?

d ..... does Fugly Floom go to the hospital?

e ..... does Thelonius throw Babe?

f ..... is the poodle unhappy?

g ..... is the boss now?

9 Who is angry when Mrs Hoggett calls Babe in the street? Why are they angry?

Chapters 6–8

Before you read

10 Will Ferdinand find Babe? How?

11 Find these words in your dictionary:

   balcony   braces   chandelier   lock   research   van

   a Which

   – do you see when you look up?

   – do people drive?

   – do some men wear?

   b What do people *lock*?

   c Why do people do *research*?

After you read

12 Who says these words? Who are they talking about?

   a 'I know that song!'

   b 'Be careful. Orang-utans are very strong.'

   c 'He'll have an accident! Let's go!'

   d 'What did the animals do to *her*?'

   e 'The animals were better than this noise.'

Writing

13 The woman across the river calls the police when she hears the animals in the Flealands Hotel. Is she right? Why (not)? What do you think?

14 You are a child in hospital when Fugly Floom visits. What happened? Did the visit make you happy? Write a letter to a friend about it.

15 Look at the pictures of Hoggett Hollow on page 1 and Flealands Hotel on page 7. Write about these places.

16 Did you like the book? What did you like? What did you not like?